Numbers

1. Write in words:

a. **573** _____

_____

b. **809** _____

_____

c. **4016** _____

_____

2. Write in figures:

a. three thousand, five hundred and sixty-two

_____

b. six thousand, two hundred and five

_____

c. one thousand and two

_____

3. What is the numeral in each circle worth in these 4-digit numbers?

a. **7 ⑥ 2 1** _____

b. **3 0 2 ⑤** _____

c. **⑨ 2 8 6** _____

d. **8 3 ④ 2** _____

e. **4 ⑨ 2 6** _____

4. Make the largest number you can using the four digits in each part.

a. **4, 6, 5, 8** _____

b. **2, 8, 9, 4** _____

c. **3, 7, 2, 1** _____

d. **2, 0, 7, 9** _____

e. **6, 7, 5, 7** _____

5. Make the smallest number you can using the four digits in each part.

a. **5, 8, 5, 7** _____

b. **9, 7, 6, 9** _____

c. **7, 2, 5, 1** _____

d. **8, 1, 6, 4** _____

6. How much larger is

a. **862** than **62**? _____

b. **345** than **5**? _____

c. **694** than **90**? _____

d. **739** than **37**? _____

7. Write these numbers in order starting with the smallest.

3261, 3049, 3847, 3205

_____

8. Round these numbers to the nearest 100.

a. **564** _____ b. **787** _____

c. **826** _____ d. **915** _____

Shape

1. What do all these shapes have in common?

_____

_____

2. Put a cross on **all** the right angles in the following shapes.

3. Draw a triangle with 3 equal sides.

What is it called?

_____

4. Use this shape to make a design on this tile. You can turn it around and repeat it in as many squares as you wish.

5. Which 3-D shape can be made from this net?

_____

6. Colour the hexagons.

Perimeters

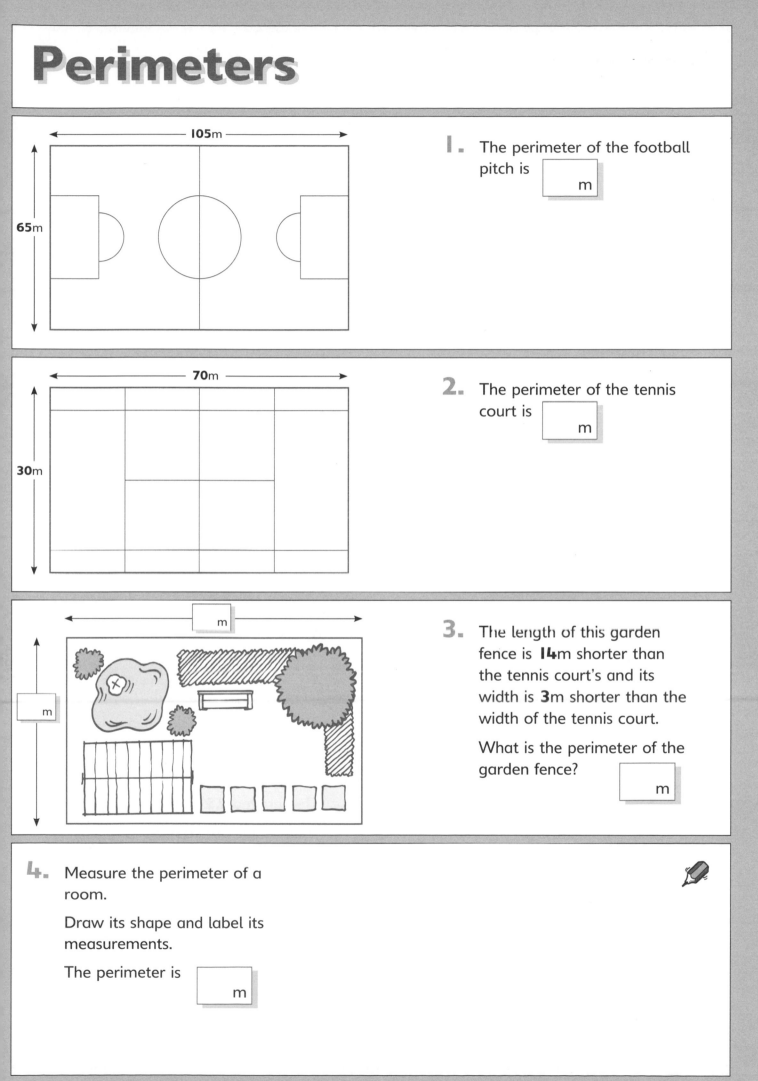

1. The perimeter of the football pitch is [ ] m

2. The perimeter of the tennis court is [ ] m

3. The length of this garden fence is **14**m shorter than the tennis court's and its width is **3**m shorter than the width of the tennis court.

   What is the perimeter of the garden fence? [ ] m

4. Measure the perimeter of a room.

   Draw its shape and label its measurements.

   The perimeter is [ ] m

What time?

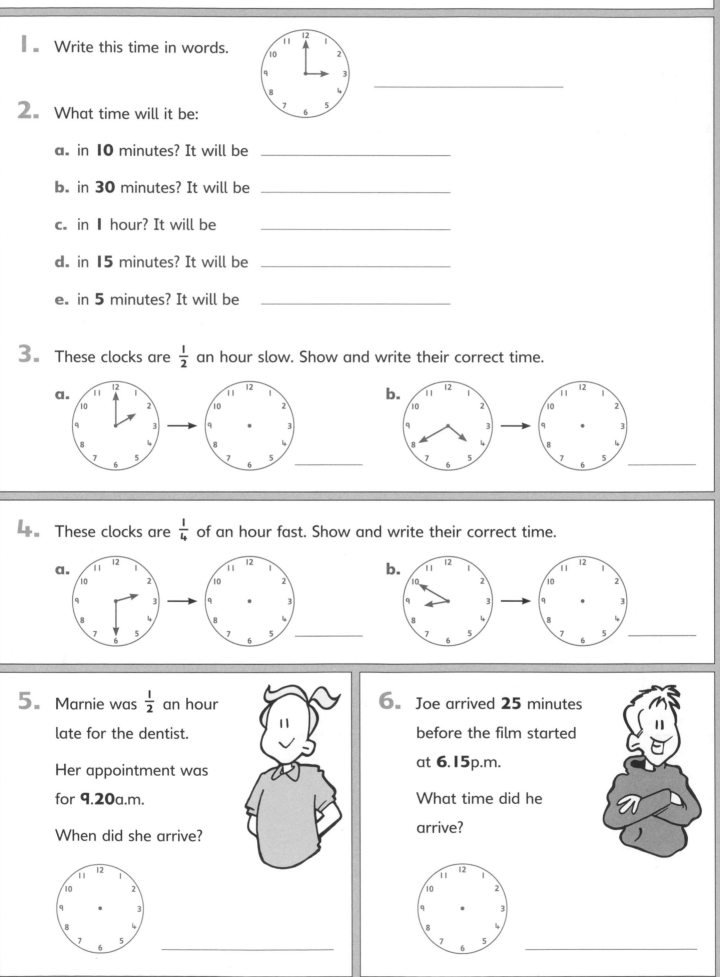

1. Write this time in words.

   _____

2. What time will it be:

   a. in **10** minutes? It will be _____

   b. in **30** minutes? It will be _____

   c. in **1** hour? It will be _____

   d. in **15** minutes? It will be _____

   e. in **5** minutes? It will be _____

3. These clocks are $\frac{1}{2}$ an hour slow. Show and write their correct time.

   a. _____

   b. _____

4. These clocks are $\frac{1}{4}$ of an hour fast. Show and write their correct time.

   a. _____

   b. _____

5. Marnie was $\frac{1}{2}$ an hour late for the dentist.

   Her appointment was for **9.20**a.m.

   When did she arrive?

   _____

6. Joe arrived **25** minutes before the film started at **6.15**p.m.

   What time did he arrive?

   _____

Coordinates

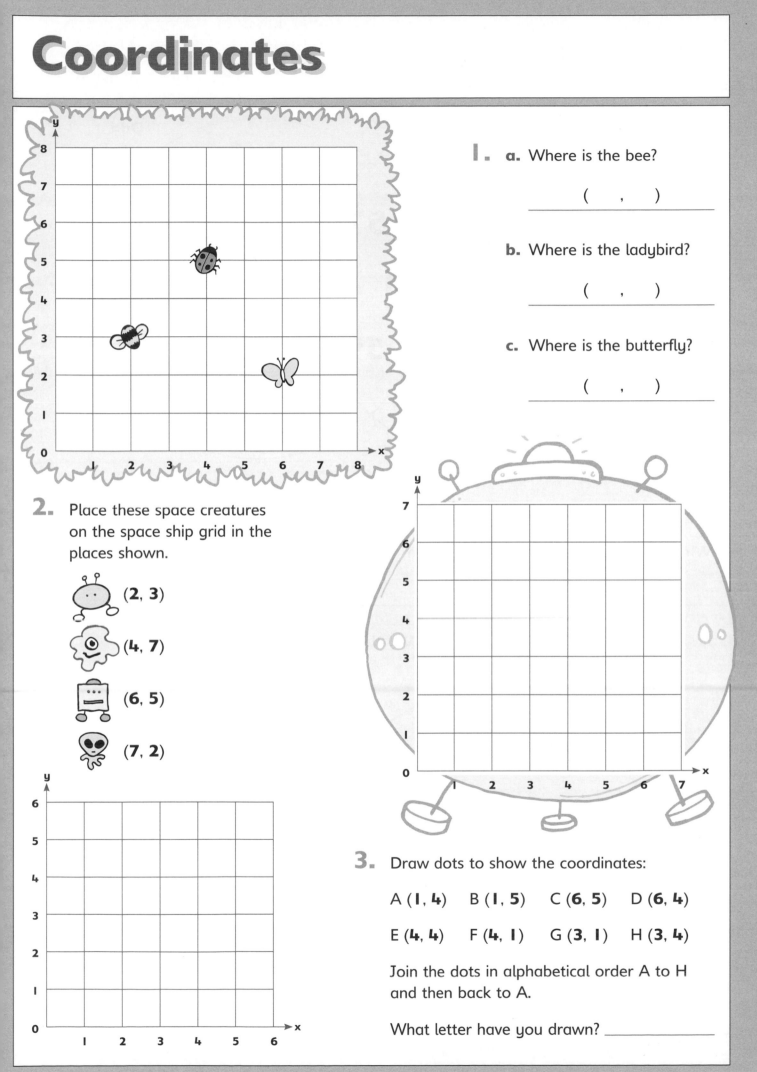

1. **a.** Where is the bee?

   _____ (,   )

   b. Where is the ladybird?

   _____ (,   )

   c. Where is the butterfly?

   _____ (,   )

2. Place these space creatures on the space ship grid in the places shown.

   (**2, 3**)

   (**4, 7**)

   (**6, 5**)

   (**7, 2**)

3. Draw dots to show the coordinates:

   A (**1, 4**)   B (**1, 5**)   C (**6, 5**)   D (**6, 4**)

   E (**4, 4**)   F (**4, 1**)   G (**3, 1**)   H (**3, 4**)

   Join the dots in alphabetical order A to H and then back to A.

   What letter have you drawn? _____

Venn Diagrams

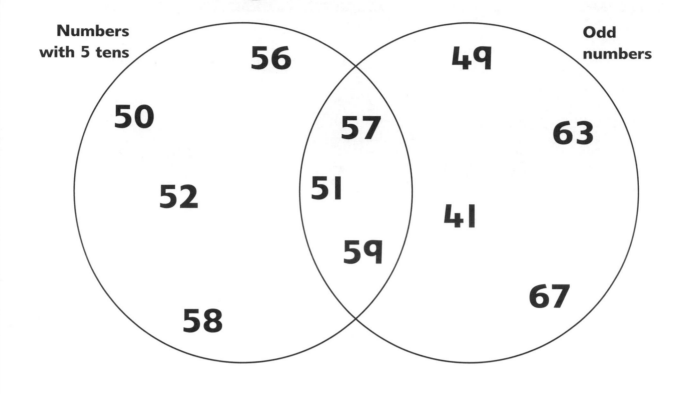

Add these numbers to the correct places in the Venn diagram: **43**, **61**, **54**, **53**, **47**

Why are there numbers in the intersection?

Fill in the numbers **68**, **70**, **71**, **75**, **76**, **80** and **84** in the Venn diagram below:

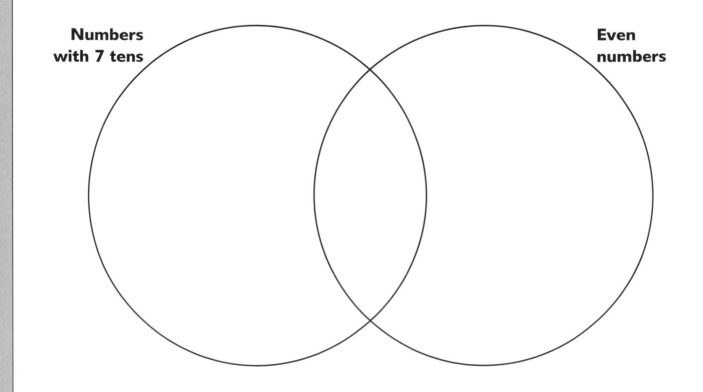

Symmetry

1. Draw these shapes in the correct area in this Venn diagram.

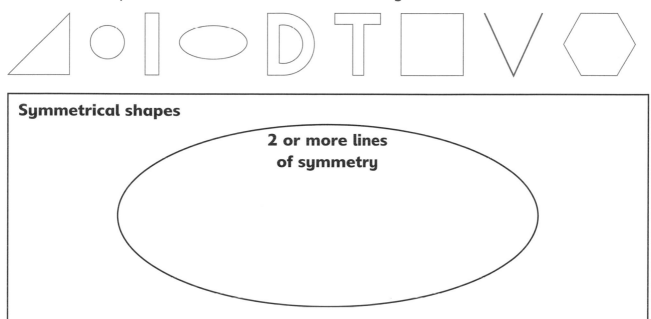

Symmetrical shapes

**2 or more lines
of symmetry**

2. Draw the mirror images.

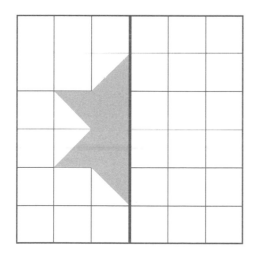

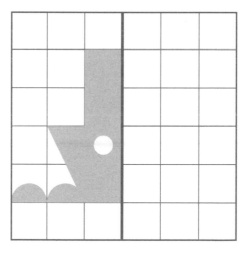

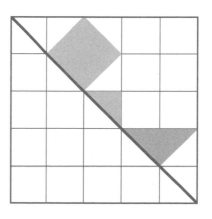

Multiples

1. Sort these multiples of **7** and **9** into the Carroll diagram.

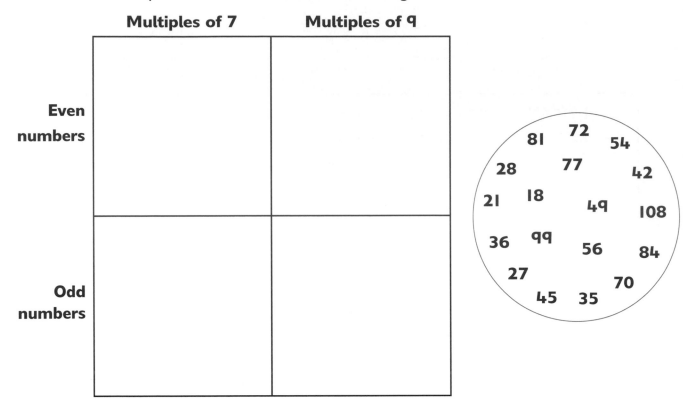

	Multiples of 7	Multiples of 9
Even numbers		
Odd numbers		

Numbers: 81, 72, 54, 28, 77, 42, 21, 18, 49, 108, 36, 99, 56, 84, 27, 70, 45, 35

2. Sort these multiples of **3** and **8** into the Carroll diagram.

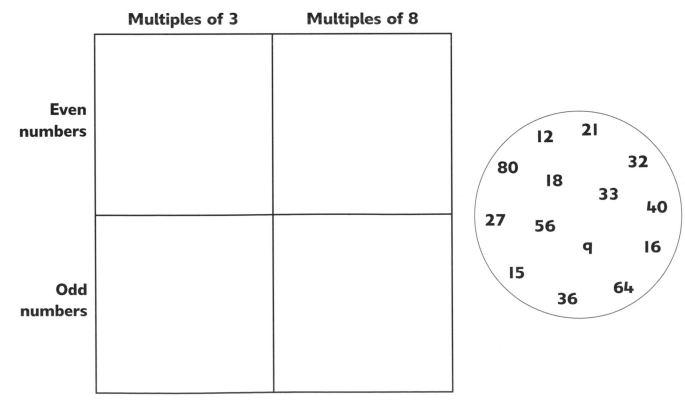

	Multiples of 3	Multiples of 8
Even numbers		
Odd numbers		

Numbers: 12, 21, 80, 32, 18, 33, 40, 27, 56, 9, 16, 15, 64, 36

Explain why one of the boxes is empty.

_____

Time

1. Show these times on the clocks

   a. 5.25 **b. 7.40** **c. 12.16** **d. 9.45**

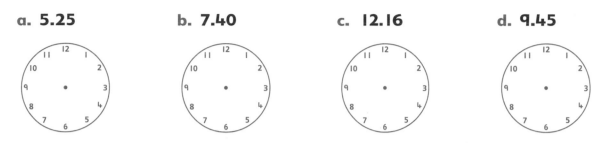

2. Write the time on the digital clocks below.

   a. p.m. **b. a.m.** **c. a.m.** **d. p.m.**

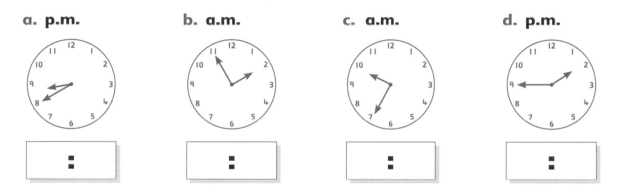

3. Trains run from Henwood to Cookfield every **30** minutes. Each train takes **15** minutes to travel between the stations.

   a. Complete the timetable.

HENWOOD	9.00		10.00	
WOODEND	9.15			
BELLFORD	9.30			
KINGHAM	9.45	10.15		
COOKFIELD	10.00			

   You arrive at Bellford Station at **10.05**a.m.

   b. How long do you wait for a train?

   c. What time does it arrive at Cookfield?

   d. The **10.00**a.m. train from Henwood is **10** minutes late.
   What time does it arrive in Kingham?

   e. The fare from Henwood to Cookfield is £**2.50** return.

   2 people cost £ .   **5** people cost £ .   **10** people cost £ .

Number Puzzles

1. Write the missing numbers so that all the answers in the addition wheel make **500**.

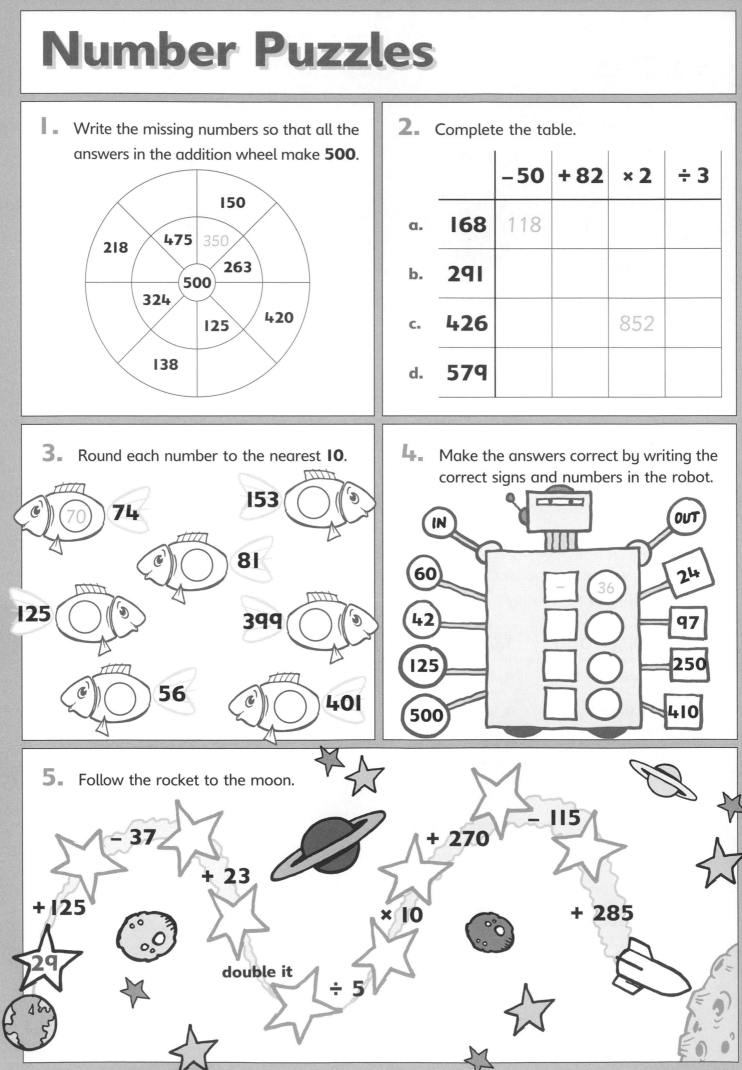

150
218 475 350
263
500
324
420
125
138

2. Complete the table.

	− 50	+ 82	× 2	÷ 3
a.	**168**	118		
b.	**291**			
c.	**426**		852	
d.	**579**			

3. Round each number to the nearest **10**.

70 **74**

153

81

125

399

56

401

4. Make the answers correct by writing the correct signs and numbers in the robot.

IN   OUT

60   24

42   97

125   250

500   410

−   36

5. Follow the rocket to the moon.

− 37

+ 23

+ 125

29

double it

÷ 5

× 10

+ 270

− 115

+ 285

Area

1. Each square is **1** square centimetre (sq. cm). How many square centimetres are there in each blue shape?

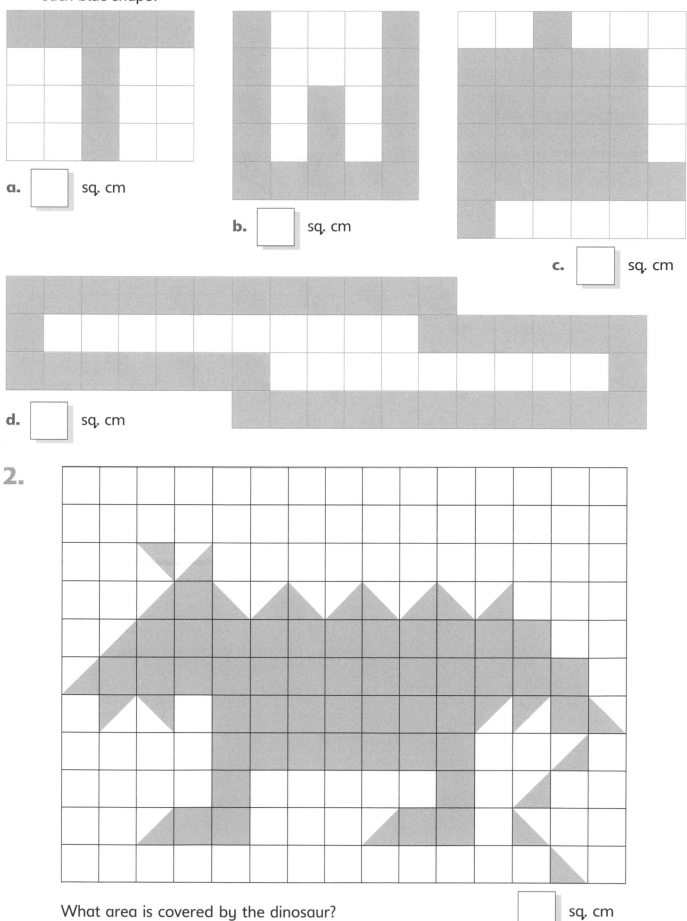

a. ☐ sq. cm

b. ☐ sq. cm

c. ☐ sq. cm

d. ☐ sq. cm

2.

What area is covered by the dinosaur? ☐ sq. cm

Walking to school

During June some children walked to school.

Each 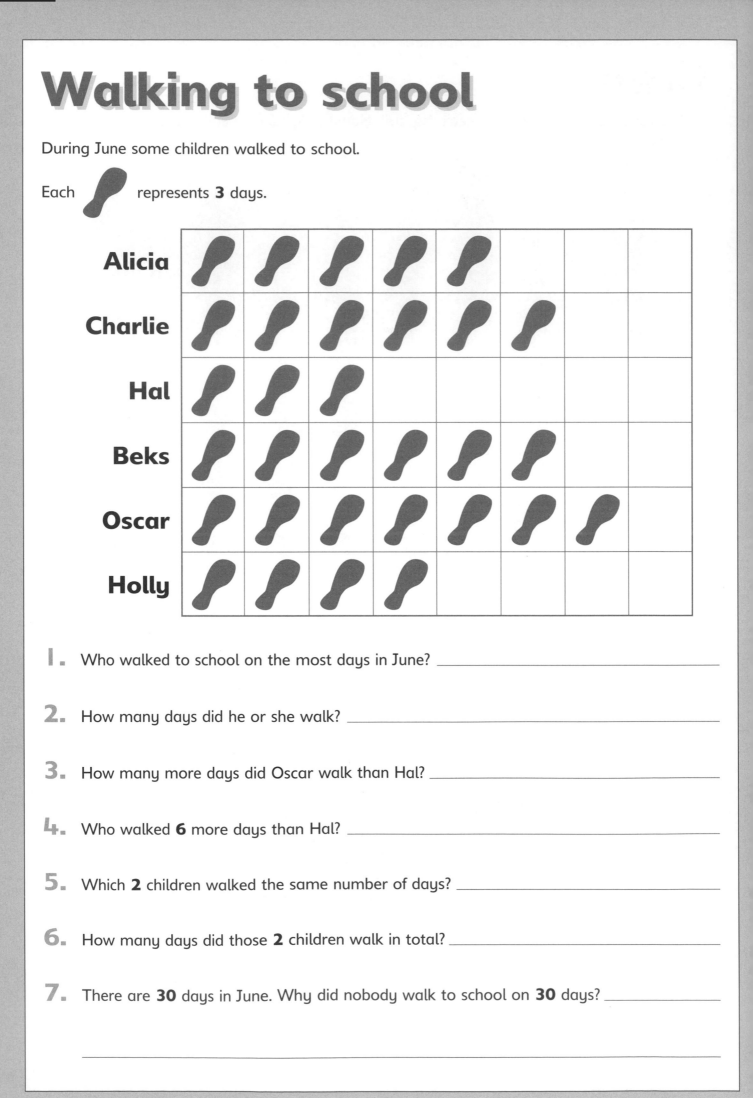 represents **3** days.

Alicia	👣	👣	👣	👣	👣		
Charlie	👣	👣	👣	👣	👣	👣	
Hal	👣	👣	👣				
Beks	👣	👣	👣	👣	👣	👣	
Oscar	👣	👣	👣	👣	👣	👣	👣
Holly	👣	👣	👣	👣			

1. Who walked to school on the most days in June? _____

2. How many days did he or she walk? _____

3. How many more days did Oscar walk than Hal? _____

4. Who walked **6** more days than Hal? _____

5. Which **2** children walked the same number of days? _____

6. How many days did those **2** children walk in total? _____

7. There are **30** days in June. Why did nobody walk to school on **30** days? _____

_____

14

Pull-out Answers

Page 3

1. a. Five hundred and seventy-three
   b. Eight hundred and nine
   c. Four thousand and sixteen

2. a. **3562**
   b. **6205**
   c. **1002**

3. a. **600**
   b. **5** units
   c. **9000**
   d. **40**
   e. **900**

4. a. **8654**
   b. **9842**
   c. **7321**
   d. **9720**
   e. **7765**

5. a. **5578**
   b. **6799**
   c. **1257**
   d. **1468**

6. a. **800**
   b. **340**
   c. **604**
   d. **702**

7. 3049, 3205,
   3261, 3847

8. a. **600** b. **800**
   c. **800** d. **900**

Page 4

1. They all have at least one right angle

2.

3.

equilateral triangle

4. Various designs

5. A cube

6.

Page 5

1. **340**m
2. **200**m
3. length = **56**m, width = **27**m, perimeter = **166**m
4. various answers

Page 6

1. **3** o'clock or **3.00**

2. a. **10** past **3** or **3.10**
   b. $\frac{1}{2}$ past **3** or **3.30**
   c. **4** o'clock or **4.00**
   d. $\frac{1}{4}$ past **3** or **3.15**
   e. **5** past **3** or **3.05**

3. a.
   $\frac{1}{2}$ past **2** or **2.30**

   b.
   10 past **5** or **5.10**

4. a.
   $\frac{1}{4}$ past **2** or **2.15**

   b.
   25 to **9** or **8.35**

5. **9.50**a.m.

6. **5.50**p.m.

Page 7

1. a. **(2,3)**
   b. **(4,5)**
   c. **(6,2)**

2.

3.

The letter is **T**

AI

Page 8

1. **54** in the left section, **53** in the centre, and **43**, **47** and **61** in the right section.
   The numbers in the intersection are odd numbers which have **5** tens.

2. Numbers with **7** tens   Even numbers

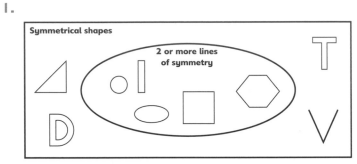

Page 9

1.

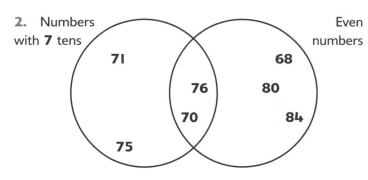

2.

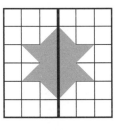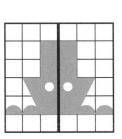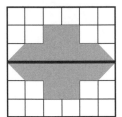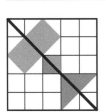

Page 10

1.

42 28 84	54 72 36
70 56	18 108
77 49 35	45 81 99
21	27

2.

36 18	64 56 80
12	40 32 16
9 27 21	
15 33	

The bottom right box is empty because all multiples of **8** are even numbers.

Page 11

1. a.   b.   c.   d.

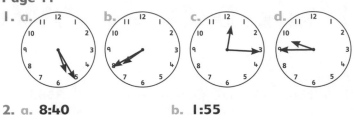

2. a. **8:40**   b. **1:55**
   c. **9:35**   d. **1:45**

3. a.

HENWOOD	9.00	9.30	10.00	10.30
WOODEND	9.15	9.45	10.15	10.45
BELLFORD	9.30	10.00	10.30	11.00
KINGHAM	9.45	10.15	10.45	11.15
COOKFIELD	10.00	10.30	11.00	11.30

b. **25** minutes
c. **11.00**
d. **10.55**
e. **2** people cost **£5.00**, **5** people cost **£12.50**, **10** people cost **£25.00**

Page 12

1.

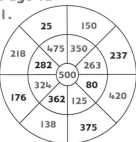

	− 50	+ 82	× 2	÷ 3
168	118	250	336	56
291	241	373	582	97
426	376	508	852	142
579	529	661	1158	193

3.

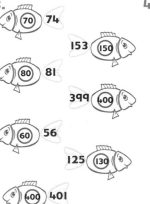

4. − 36
   + 55
   × 2 or + 125
   − 90

5. **154 , 117 , 140 , 280 , 56 , 560 , 830 , 715 , 1000**

Page 13

1. a. **8** sq. cm   b. **15** sq. cm   c. **23** sq. cm
   d. **38** sq. cm

2. **58** sq. cm

Page 14

1. Oscar
2. **21** days
3. **12** days
4. Alicia
5. Charlie and Beks
6. **36** days
7. Because they don't go to school at the weekends

Page 15

1. a. answer will depend on child's circumstances
   b. impossible
   c. answer will depend on child's circumstances
   d. probable
   e. possible (if Arthur is visiting a zoo or a foreign country, say)
   f. impossible

2. a. certain/likely (unless there is a holiday next week!)
   b. unlikely (unless the TV is very unreliable)
   c. impossible
   d. certain (unless for cultural reasons birthday cards are not sent)
   e. impossible (for most mums, but other answers acceptable!)

3. Various answers for each part.

Page 16

1. a. **147** miles
   b. **294** miles
2. to Alnwick **29**
   to Newcastle **59**

3. **97** miles
4. **38** miles

Page 17

5. a. **4** coaches
   b. yes, **7** spare seats

6. a. **21** adults
   b. **4** cars

7. **13** girls

8. **41** children

9. **8.30**p.m.

Page 18

1. Saturday
2. Thursday
3. **90**
4. **570**
5. **30**

Page 19

6. **240**
7. **120**
8.

	Total present	Number of adults	Number of children	Cost of programmes
Thursday	120	80	40	£40.00
Friday	210	160	50	£80.00
Saturday	240	120	120	£60.00

9. **210** children
10. **£180.00**
11. Thursday **6** rows, Friday **11** rows (accept $10\frac{1}{2}$ rows), Saturday **12** rows

Page 20

1. a. $9\frac{1}{2}$ hours   b. $62\frac{1}{2}$ hours
2. **17** days
3. **288** hours
4. length   **25**m
   width   **12**m
   perimeter   **74**m
   area of water surface   **300**m²

5. **32** lengths, **800**m

Page 21

6. a. Children **1400**, Adults **240**
   b. **1160**
7. a. **£237.00**
   b. **£262.50**
   c. **£499.50**
8. a. Sunday
   b. **£289.50**
9. a. **£2.75**
   b. **£1.10**

Page 22

1. Many possible answers, e.g.

   100 × 50   1628 + 3372   40 × 125

   3273 + 1727   3564 + 1436   20 × 250

   20 × (200 + 50)   200 × 25   1525 + 3475

2. a. 92
   b. 80
   c. 12
   d. 14
   e. 460

3. a. $\frac{1}{4}$
   b. $\frac{3}{4}$
   c. $\frac{6}{10}$ or $\frac{3}{5}$
   d. $\frac{55}{100}$ or $\frac{11}{20}$
   e. $\frac{4}{10}$ or $\frac{2}{5}$
   f. $\frac{15}{100}$ or $\frac{3}{20}$

4. a. 50°
   b. 145°
   c. 105°

5. a. 142, 149
   b. 500, 0
   c. 124, 130
   d. 764, 752

Page 23

1. a. $\frac{1}{4}$ and $\frac{2}{8}$ circled
   b. $\frac{4}{8}$ and $\frac{1}{2}$ circled
   c. $\frac{2}{6}$ and $\frac{3}{9}$ circled
   d. $\frac{8}{10}$ and $\frac{4}{5}$ circled

2. a. $\frac{7}{100}$ $\frac{1}{5}$ $\frac{1}{4}$ $\frac{3}{10}$ $\frac{1}{2}$
   b. 20%, 25%, $\frac{35}{100}$, $\frac{1}{2}$, $\frac{3}{4}$
   c. $\frac{1}{2}$, 60%, 75%, $\frac{4}{5}$, $\frac{9}{10}$

3.

| 0 | | $\frac{1}{6}$ | $\frac{1}{4}$ | | $\frac{5}{12}$ | $\frac{1}{2}$ | | $\frac{2}{3}$ | $\frac{3}{4}$ | $\frac{5}{6}$ | | 1 |

4. a. Angus 24
   b. Dad 12
   c. Mum 18
   d. Alice 6
   e. 12
   f. $\frac{12}{72}$ or $\frac{1}{6}$

5. a. $\frac{6}{12} = \frac{1}{2}$
   b. $\frac{10}{12}$ or $\frac{5}{6}$
   c. $\frac{5}{12}$
   d. $\frac{4}{12} = \frac{1}{3}$

Page 24

1. a. £33.00
   b. £36.50

2. a. £24.00
   b. £6.00
   c. Various answers
      e.g. £5 note + £1 coin or six £1 coins... etc

3. a. £10 note
   b. 250g
   c. 500g
   d. £1.98
   e. £4.02

4. £14.00

Page 25

5. a. Grandpa   £3.00
      Granny   £2.00
      Mum   £1.80
      Zoe   £1.50
      Tom   £2.40
      Total   £10.70
      Grandpa's tip: £1.07

6. a. $1\frac{1}{4}$ litres
   b. No
   c. Either they asked for the jug to be refilled or they shared it out evenly so they all had a little less.

7. a. £12.00
   b. £8.00
   c. $\frac{1}{4}$ to 4 or 3:45

8. a. various
   b. various, depending on the answers to part a.

Page 26

1. a. 5kg   b. 2kg   c. 11kg

2. Butter 300g
   Syrup 6 tablespoons
   Sugar 360g
   Coconut 225g
   Oats 225g
   Flour 405g
   Bicarb 3 teaspoons
   Water 3 tablespoons

3. a. C and F
   b. A and B
   c. D and E
   d. B and E

4. a. 33·8kg
   b. 37·55kg

5. Frankie 4kg
   Les 8kg
   Stan 0
   Pat 6kg

Page 27

1. 12

2. a. 30kg
   b. 22·5kg

3. 18

4. 6·85kg

5. 15

6. 119

Probability

1. How likely are these things to happen? Choose a word from the box.

> probable   possible   impossible

a.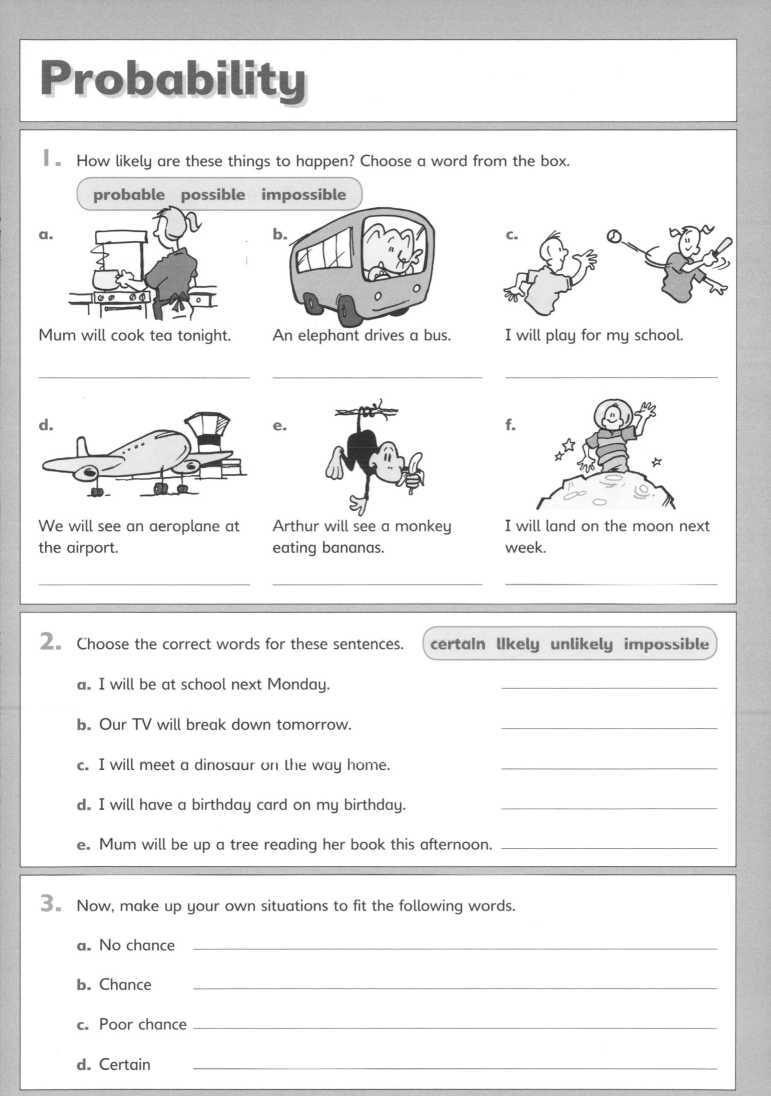

Mum will cook tea tonight.

_____

b.

An elephant drives a bus.

_____

c.

I will play for my school.

_____

d.

We will see an aeroplane at the airport.

_____

e.

Arthur will see a monkey eating bananas.

_____

f.

I will land on the moon next week.

_____

2. Choose the correct words for these sentences.

> certain   likely   unlikely   impossible

a. I will be at school next Monday.   _____

b. Our TV will break down tomorrow.   _____

c. I will meet a dinosaur on the way home.   _____

d. I will have a birthday card on my birthday. _____

e. Mum will be up a tree reading her book this afternoon. _____

3. Now, make up your own situations to fit the following words.

a. No chance   _____

b. Chance   _____

c. Poor chance _____

d. Certain   _____

15

Coach Journeys

This table shows the distances in miles travelled between Berwick and York.

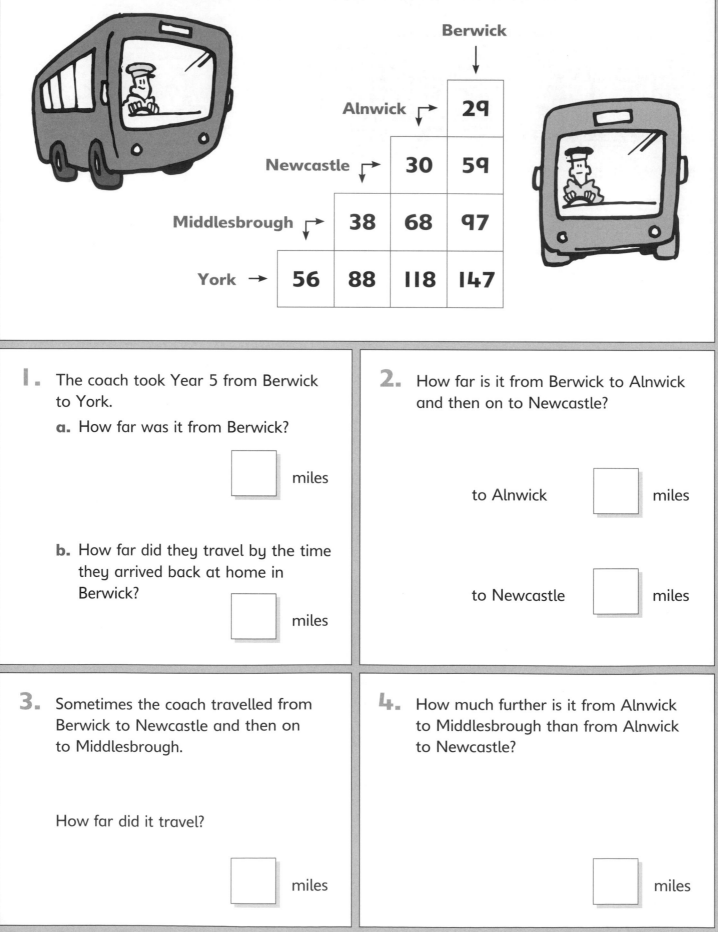

	Berwick			
Alnwick →	29			
Newcastle →	30	59		
Middlesbrough →	38	68	97	
York →	56	88	118	147

1. The coach took Year 5 from Berwick to York.

   a. How far was it from Berwick?

   ☐ miles

   b. How far did they travel by the time they arrived back at home in Berwick?

   ☐ miles

2. How far is it from Berwick to Alnwick and then on to Newcastle?

   to Alnwick ☐ miles

   to Newcastle ☐ miles

3. Sometimes the coach travelled from Berwick to Newcastle and then on to Middlesbrough.

   How far did it travel?

   ☐ miles

4. How much further is it from Alnwick to Middlesbrough than from Alnwick to Newcastle?

   ☐ miles

5. This coach holds **53** people. A school in York is taking **205** children to Alnwick Castle.

  a. How many coaches will they need? ☐

  b. Will they have any spare seats? _____

    If yes, how many? _____

6. There needs to be **1** adult to every **10** children.

  a. How many adults are needed? _____

  b. Every spare seat needs to be occupied by an adult. The remaining adults travel by car, with **4** people in a car, how many cars do they need to take? _____

7. There are **96** boys on the coaches.

  How many more girls are there? _____

8. When they reach Alnwick Castle the children will be put into **5** groups. How many children will be in each group? _____

9. The journey from school to Alnwick takes **4** hours. They set off at **9**a.m. and spend $3\frac{1}{2}$ hours at the Castle. What time do they arrive back at school?

Year 5 School Play

Number of people in the audience

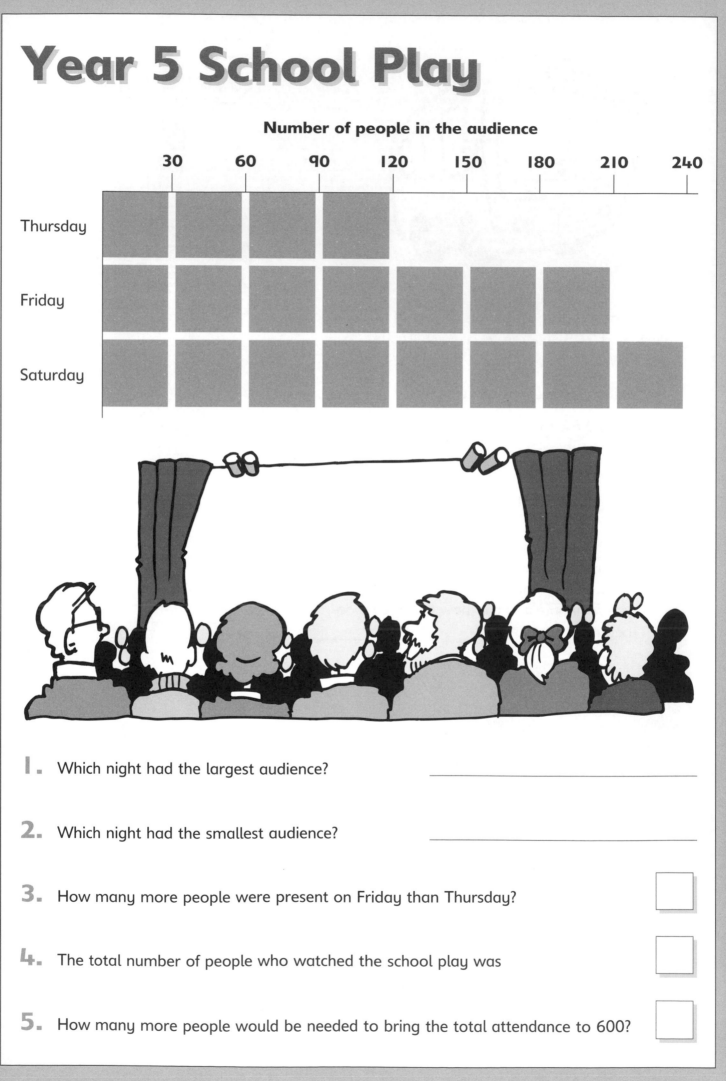

| | 30 | 60 | 90 | 120 | 150 | 180 | 210 | 240 |

Thursday

Friday

Saturday

1. Which night had the largest audience? _____

2. Which night had the smallest audience? _____

3. How many more people were present on Friday than Thursday?

4. The total number of people who watched the school play was

5. How many more people would be needed to bring the total attendance to 600?

6. **80** programmes were sold on Thursday and double that number on Friday. What was the total sold for those **2** nights?

7. On Saturday they sold $\frac{1}{2}$ of the number of programmes sold on Thursday and Friday altogether. How many were sold on Saturday?

8. Each night every adult but none of the children bought a programme costing **50**p. Use the graph and your answer to questions **6** and **7** to work out how many adults and children were at each performance and the cost of programmes for the three evenings. Record your answers in the table below.

	Total present	Number of adults	Number of children	Cost of programmes
Thursday				
Friday				
Saturday				

9. The total number of children who attended is ☐

10. The total cost of programmes is ☐

11. If **1** row holds **20** people, how many rows do they need for each night?

Thursday ☐   Friday ☐   Saturday ☐

At the Swimming Pool

HOURS OF OPENING

Monday to Friday 9.00a.m. – 9.30p.m.

Saturday 1.00p.m. – 4.00p.m.

Sunday 9.30a.m. – 4.00p.m.

1. For how many hours is the pool open during

   a. the weekend?

   b. Monday to Friday?

2. The pool is closed for a fortnight for cleaning in October.
   On how many days is it open during that month?

3. For how many hours is the pool open in February in a non-leap year?

4. Here is a plan of the swimming pool.

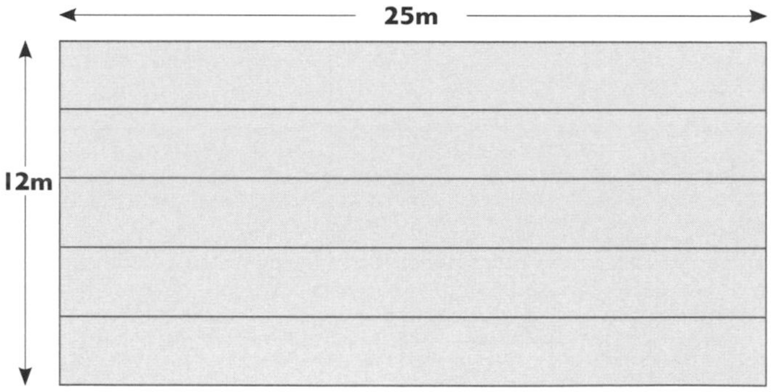

   25m

   12m

   Fill in the table below.

length	
width	
perimeter	
area of water surface	

5. The pool is often used for relay races. There are **4** children in each team. They each swim **2** lengths of the pool. There are **4** teams.

   In total the teams swim

    lengths, a distance of m

This table shows the number of swimmers for the 3rd week in May 2005.

	Sun	Mon	Tues	Wed	Thurs	Fri	Sat	Admission
Adults	105	6	7	10	8	9	95	**Adult £2.50**
Children	237	252	196	185	109	215	206	**Children £1.00**

6. **a.** Work out the total numbers of people visiting the pool during the week.

Children ☐

Adults ☐

b. How many more children than adults visited this week? ☐

7. How much money did the Swimming Pool take on Sunday?

a. for children ☐

b. for adults ☐

c. in total ☐

8. **a.** On which day during the week did they take the most money? _____

b. How much more money did they take on this day than on Wednesday? ☐

9. If prices increased by **10**% during the same week in **2006** how much would the cost of entry be for

a. Adults ☐

b. Children ☐

Numbers

1. Using some of the numbers below and any operations, find as many ways as possible to make **5000**.

100	1628	40	3273
3564	20	200	1525
250	1727	125	50
3372	25	3475	1436

_____

_____

_____

_____

_____

2. a. $\frac{1}{10}$ of **920** = ☐

b. $\frac{1}{8}$ of **640** = ☐

c. $\frac{3}{8}$ of **32** = ☐

d. $\frac{2}{7}$ of **49** = ☐

e. $\frac{4}{5}$ of **575** = ☐

3. **Number Factory.** Change the decimal fractions into vulgar fractions. The first is done for you.

0·25 → $\frac{1}{4}$ a.

0·75 → ☐ b.

0·6 → ☐ c.

0·55 → ☐ d.

0·40 → ☐ e.

0·15 → ☐ f.

4. What are the missing angles?

a. 130° ? ☐

b. 35° ? ☐

c. ? 75° ☐

5. Continue the number patterns.

a. 121   128   135   ____   ____

b. 2000   1500   1000   ____   ____

c. 106   112   118   ____   ____

d. 800   788   776   ____   ____

Fractions

1. Circle the two fractions which are equivalent in each line.

a. $\frac{5}{8}$ $\frac{3}{8}$ $\frac{1}{4}$ $\frac{2}{8}$ $\frac{2}{5}$

b. $\frac{4}{8}$ $\frac{4}{5}$ $\frac{1}{2}$ $\frac{4}{6}$ $\frac{7}{12}$

c. $\frac{2}{3}$ $\frac{2}{6}$ $\frac{6}{12}$ $\frac{3}{9}$ $\frac{5}{12}$

d. $\frac{3}{5}$ $\frac{8}{10}$ $\frac{6}{8}$ $\frac{6}{10}$ $\frac{4}{5}$

2. Write these fractions and percentages in value order from lowest to highest.

a. $\frac{7}{100}$ $\frac{1}{2}$ $\frac{1}{4}$ $\frac{1}{5}$ $\frac{3}{10}$

_____

b. $\frac{1}{2}$ 25% $\frac{35}{100}$ 20% $\frac{3}{4}$

_____

c. $\frac{4}{5}$ 60% $\frac{9}{10}$ $\frac{1}{2}$ 75%

_____

3. Write these fractions in the correct places on the number line:

$\frac{1}{4}$ $\frac{2}{3}$ $\frac{5}{6}$ $\frac{3}{4}$ $\frac{1}{6}$ $\frac{5}{12}$

0 $\frac{1}{2}$ **1**

4. Mum bought a bunch of grapes with **72** grapes on it. The family shared part of this bunch in the following way. Work out how many grapes they each had.

a. Angus had $\frac{1}{3}$ ☐

b. Dad had $\frac{1}{6}$ ☐

c. Mum had $\frac{1}{4}$ ☐

d. Alice had $\frac{1}{12}$ ☐

e. How many grapes were left on the bunch? ☐

f. What fraction of the bunch was left? ☐

5. Look at the clowns. Answer the questions as fractions in their lowest terms. How many clowns ...

a. ... are wearing pointed hats? ☐

b. ... are holding balloons? ☐

c. ... have flowers in their hats? ☐

d. ... are wearing bowler hats? ☐

At the Zoo

1. 10-year-old twins, Zoe and Tom went to the zoo with Mum, Grandpa and Granny.

   a. How much did it cost them to get in? £ _____

   b. They also bought one copy of the Guide Book. How much did they spend altogether? £ _____

2. The family went in the Reptile House.

   a. What was the total cost? £ _____

   b. Grandpa gave Zoe three **£10** notes to pay. How much change did Zoe have? £ _____

   c. How could the change be given? _____

3. The children went in the Bird House. Granny gave them a note to pay. They had **£6.00** change.

   a. What value of note did she given them? £ _____

The two children then used the change to buy a $\frac{1}{4}$ kg bag of bird seed each.

   b. How many grams in $\frac{1}{4}$ kg? _____ g

   c. How much did the **2** bags of seed weigh? _____ g

   d. How much did the **2** bags of seed cost? £ _____

   e. How much change did Granny now have? £ _____

4. While Grandpa had a coffee, the rest of the family went into the Butterfly House.

How much change was there out of a **£20** note? £ _____

REFRESHMENTS		SOUVENIRS	
Apple	30p	Card	50p
Coffee	£1.25	Pencil	70p
Chips	£1.10	Notebook	90p
Sausages	£1.90	Pencil Sharpener	£1.25
Beans	50p	Mug	£4.00
Sandwich	£1.80	Book	£5.00
Soup	£1.20	Fridge Magnet	£2.50
Pasta Salad	£2.00		

5. This is what the family had for lunch. Make out their bill.

Grandpa	Sausage and chips	_____
Granny	Pasta Salad	_____
Mum	Sandwich	_____
Zoe	Soup and apple	_____
Tom	Sausage and beans	_____
	Total	_____

Grandpa left a **10%** tip. How much is this? _____

6. On every table in the cafe, there was a **1** litre jug of water. Each glass held $\frac{1}{4}$ of a litre. All the family had a glass of water each.

a. How much water would the 5 glasses hold? ☐

b. Was there enough water in the jug? yes / no

c. If no, what do you think they did? _____

7. At $\frac{1}{4}$ past **3** the family went on a **30**-minute boat ride.

a. How much did it cost? £ ☐

b. How much change did they get from a **£20** note? £ ☐

c. At what time did they get off the boat? ☐

8. At the end of the day they went to the souvenir shop. Zoe and Tom had **£10** each to spend.

a. What do you think they bought?

Zoe _____

Tom _____

b. How much change did they have?

Zoe _____

Tom _____

Mass

1. Round all these measurements to the nearest kg.

a. Mum bought a bag of potatoes weighing **5·35**kg.

b. I had a **1·55**kg box of chocolates for Christmas.

c. The farmer weighed the sack of turnips at **10·95**kg.

_____   _____   _____

2. Mum's recipe is for **30** biscuits. She wishes to make **90** biscuits. Change the recipe.

new quantities

100g butter ⟶ ☐

2 tablespoons syrup ⟶ ☐

120g sugar ⟶ ☐

75g coconut ⟶ ☐

75g oats ⟶ ☐

135g flour ⟶ ☐

1 tsp bicarb of soda ⟶ ☐

1 tbsp of hot water ⟶ ☐

3.

| 1·15 kg A | 4·10 kg B | 1·25 kg C |
| 1·95 kg D | 4·05 kg E | 1¼ kg F |

Which **2** parcels together weigh...?

a. $2\frac{1}{2}$ kg _____ and _____

b. **5·25**kg _____ and _____

c. **6**kg _____ and _____

d. **8·15**kg _____ and _____

4. Sheila the sheep normally weighs **36·3**kg.

a. She lost **2·5**kg so she then weighed ☐

b. Then, she put on **3·75**kg which brought her weight to ☐

5. Jockeys are weighed before each race. In some races each jockey's weight is made up to the heaviest jockey's weight by adding weights. Complete the table.

	Weight	Added Weight
Frankie	**52**kg	
Les	**48**kg	
Stan	**56**kg	
Pat	**50**kg	

Word Problems

1. I think of a number and multiply it by **9**.

The answer is **108**.

What is my number?

2. There is **1·5**kg of flour in a large bag.

a. The corner shop has
20 bags on the shelf.
What is their total mass? ___ kg

b. **5** customers bought a
bag each. How much
flour was left? ___ kg

3. In the farmyard there
are **3** cockerels for
every **9** hens.

There are **54** hens.

How many cockerels
are there?

4. Mr Jones had a **10**kg bag
of carrots for his **3** donkeys.

He gave the **3** donkeys **2** carrots
each every day for a week.

Each carrot weighed **75**g.

What was the weight of carrots
left at the end of the week?

5. On holiday Ellie bought
40 postcards to send to
her friends.

She sent $\frac{3}{8}$ of them on
Wednesday and $\frac{2}{5}$ of the
remaining ones on Friday.

How many did she have
left to post on Saturday?

6. I think of a number and divide it by **7**.

The answer is **17**.

What is my number?

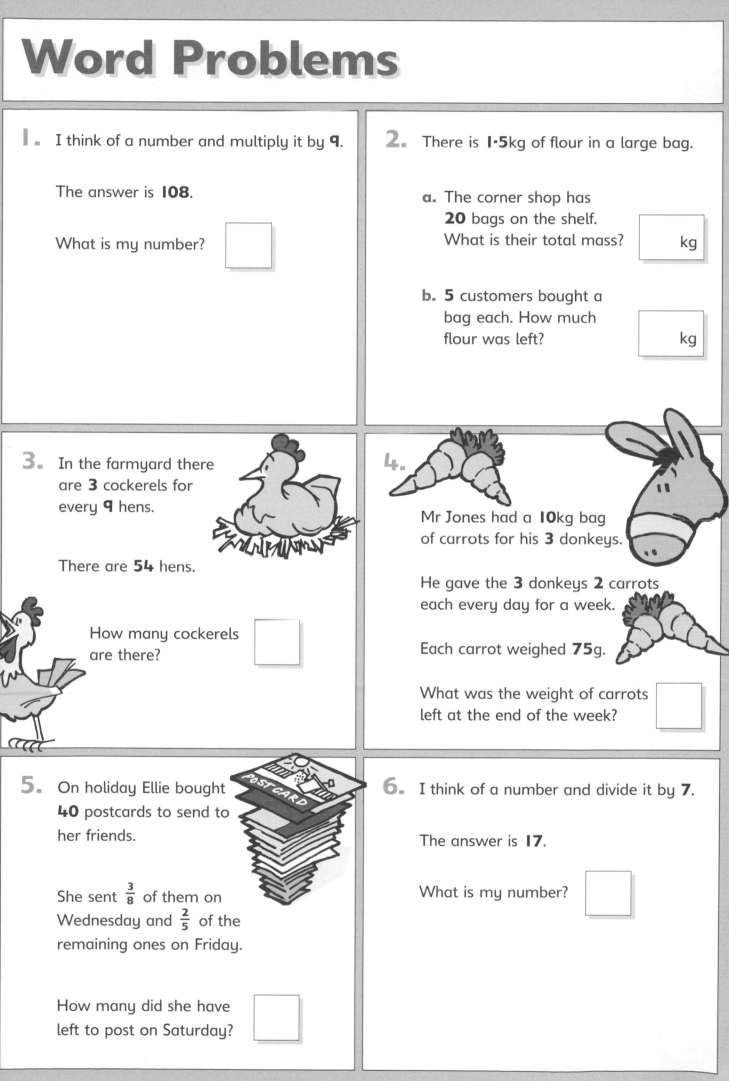

Schofield & Sims

the long-established educational publisher specialising in maths, English and science

Key Stage 2 Problem Solving is a series of graded activity books helping children to sharpen their mathematical skills. It encourages them to apply their maths skills to a range of 'real-life' situations, such as shopping and keeping score in games.

Key Stage 2 Problem Solving Book 2 covers:

- Thousands
- Area, perimeter and angles of shapes
- Coordinates
- Lines of symmetry
- Odd and even numbers, multiples of 3, 7, 8 and 9
- Fractions
- Probability.

This book is suitable for children in Key Stage 2 – particularly those in Years 4 and 5.

The full range of titles in the series is as follows:

Key Stage 2 Problem Solving Book 1 (for Years 3 and 4)   ISBN 978 07217 0935 2

Key Stage 2 Problem Solving Book 2 (for Years 4 and 5)   ISBN 978 07217 0936 9

Key Stage 2 Problem Solving Book 3 (for Years 5 and 6)   ISBN 978 07217 0937 6

Key Stage 2 Problem Solving Book 4 (for Year 6)   ISBN 978 07217 1138 6

Have you tried **Mental Arithmetic** by Schofield & Sims?
This series helps children to sharpen their calculation skills by using mathematical knowledge to solve one- and two-step number problems.

For further information and to place your order visit www.schofieldandsims.co.uk or telephone 01484 607080

ISBN 978-07217-0936-9

9 780721 709369

Schofield & Sims

Dogley Mill, Fenay Bridge, Huddersfield HD8 0NQ
Phone: 01484 607080 Facsimile: 01484 606815
E-mail: sales@schofieldandsims.co.uk
www.schofieldandsims.co.uk

MIX
Paper from responsible sources
FSC® C023114

ISBN 978 07217 0936 9

£3.50
(Retail price)

Key Stage 2
Age range 7-11 years